THE MINIATURE SCORE SERIES

THE SYMPHONIES OF HAYDN SCHUBERT AND MOZART IN SCORE

Edited and devised by

ALBERT E. WIER

The system of arrow signals and special typographical markings, employed
in this work to enable those unacquainted with the art of score reading to
follow the instrumental outline and to identify the various themes as they
appear and recur, is the subject of a pending application for Letters Patent
of the United States owned by Harcourt, Brace and Company, Inc.

BONANZA BOOKS · NEW YORK

PREFACE

For the comprehension of orchestral scores, even with the assistance of the system of arrow signals employed in this volume, ability to read instrumental music in both treble and bass clefs is necessary.

It must also be borne in mind that certain wind instruments, such as the clarinet (except the clarinet in C), the French horn (except the horn in C) and the trumpets (except the trumpet in C) are transposing instruments; also that viola and Tenor trombone parts are written in the Alto and Tenor clefs, therefore some knowledge of transposition and of these clefs will be useful.

Four separate pages of miniature score are printed on each large page of this volume. The large page is bisected by horizontal and vertical lines, the miniature pages located numerically as follows:

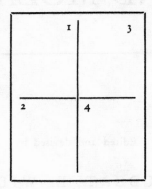

The large pages of this volume are designated by numbers in parentheses at the bottom of the pages; the miniature score pages of each symphony are numbered separately (starting with Page 1) in the upper right and left hand corners.

The opposite page contains a miniature reproduction of two pages from the score of a Haydn symphony. It will be noted that the top page comprises five bars of music with a separate line provided for each instrument, its name being noted before the line. The lower page contains two sections of scoring; this is known as score condensation because all instruments that have no notes to play during the six measures of the first section on the page are omitted, and all instruments that have no notes to play in the seven measures of the second section are omitted. The presence of two or more sections of scoring on one page is always indicated by the mark **//** between each section, and these marks must be carefully observed when reading score.

The system of arrow signals used in this volume will be easily comprehended if its purpose is fully understood before attempting to make use of them. The purpose, starting with the first measure of each symphony, is to indicate the main melodic line as it progresses from instrument to instrument in the wood-wind, brass, string and percussion sections of the orchestra. A practical example of this method of score-reading is given on the opposite page (Page 3).

In addition to the arrow signal system, the various divisions of each symphonic movement, such as **Introduction, Exposition, Development, Recapitulation, Coda,** etc., are indicated *over* the score; the names and lengths of the various themes, such as **Principal Theme, Subordinate Theme, Concluding Theme,** etc., are printed *under* the score with a wavy black line to indicate their length.

EXPLANATION OF ARROW SIGNAL SYSTEM

The pages used here for explanatory purposes are taken from the *Allegretto* of the "Military" Symphony by Josef Haydn.

The circled numbers near the arrows are used *only on this page* to aid in clarifying the explanation; they are *not* used elsewhere in the volume.

Arrows Nos. 1 & 2 indicate the appearance of the Principal Theme, Part I in the 1st violins and flute. At the bottom of the page is the name of the theme, the wavy black line indicating its length.

Arrow No. 3 indicates an ascending figure in the violas.

Arrows Nos. 4 & 5 indicate the continuance of the theme in the 1st violins and flute.

Arrows Nos. 6 & 7 indicate the repetition of the Principal Theme in the oboe and clarinet.

The Mark // indicates the separation of the page into two sections of score.

Arrows Nos. 8 & 9 indicate the continuance of the Principal Theme in the oboe and clarinet.

Arrow No. 11 points out a figure in the French horns.

Arrows Nos. 10, 12, & 13 indicate the continuance of the melodic line in the flute, 1st violins and 2nd violins.

SPECIAL NOTE
When two or more arrows are marked in the same measure, it means that the passage is to be found in other instruments at the same time, or that an important counter-theme or special musical figure is being developed. The eye can follow any one of these arrows.

The Miniature Score Series

This is the third volume in the Harcourt, Brace Miniature Score Series, presenting sixteen symphonies by Haydn, Schubert and Mozart. The first volume contains the nine symphonies of Beethoven, the second, four Brahms and three Tschaikowsky symphonies. Future volumes include a book of orchestral excerpts from Richard Wagner, a collection of ten famous symphonies by individual composers, also a volume of symphonic poems. The arrow system (in course of patent) will be continued in all these volumes.

THE EDITOR

INDEX

Preface   2

Explanation of Arrow Signal System   3

JOSEF HAYDN

Historical and Critical Comment on Haydn Symphonies   6-7

"FAREWELL" SYMPHONY   8

"OXFORD" SYMPHONY   19

"SURPRISE" SYMPHONY   35

"SALOMON" SYMPHONY   51

"MILITARY" SYMPHONY   68

"CLOCK" SYMPHONY   90

"LONDON" SYMPHONY   106

WOLFGANG AMADEUS MOZART

Historical and Critical Comment on Mozart Symphonies   125-127

"HAFFNER" SYMPHONY   128

"LINZ" SYMPHONY   146

"PRAGUE" SYMPHONY   162

SYMPHONY IN Eb MAJOR   180

SYMPHONY IN G MINOR   196

"JUPITER" SYMPHONY   213

FRANZ PETER SCHUBERT

Historical and Critical Comment on Schubert Symphonies   234-236

"UNFINISHED" SYMPHONY   237

SYMPHONY IN C MAJOR   253

SYMPHONY IN Bb MAJOR   320

HISTORICAL AND CRITICAL COMMENT ON
HAYDN SYMPHONIES

The symphonies of Josef Haydn were scored for the following instruments:.

Flauto (Flute)	*Fl.*	Timpani	*Timp.*
Oboi (Oboes)	*Ob.*	Violini (Violins)	*Vl.*
Clarinetti (Clarinets)	*Cl.*	Viola	*Vla.*
Fagotti (Bassoons)	*Fg.*	Violoncello	*Vc.*
Corni (Horns)	*Cor.*	Contrabasso (Basso)	*Cb. or B.*
Trombe (Trumpets)	*Tbe.*		

These are the names under which the instruments are listed on the first page of each score; the abbreviation used on succeeding pages follows. It will be noted that Haydn did not use trombones and employed clarinets only in the "Clock" and "London" Symphonies.

THE "FAREWELL" SYMPHONY   Page 8

Haydn wrote this symphony in 1772 during the period in which he was conductor of Prince Esterhazy's orchestra. Shortly before conceiving this work, Haydn had asked the Prince for an extended leave of absence, but His Royal Highness, anticipating the arrival of several distinguished guests for whom he wished the orchestra to perform, urged the Maestro to defer what was really a greatly needed vacation. Haydn, not to be put off, elected to reiterate his request in musical form by arranging the instrumentation of the last movement in this symphony so that one by one the players stop, pick up their instruments, turn out the lights on their desks, and walk out of the room, leaving only two violinists to play the last few bars of the movement. History has it that the "Farewell" Symphony accomplished its purpose in gaining the desired leave of absence.

THE "OXFORD" SYMPHONY   Page 19

In the period from 1787 to 1790 Haydn composed some of his greatest works, including the six "Russian" string quartets, fifteen piano trios and twelve symphonies for which he received a commission from the "Concert Spirituel", an institution founded in 1725 by Philidor. These symphonies were divided into two sets of six each; one in the second set became known as the "Oxford" Symphony because it was performed in the Sheldonian Theatre on July 8, 1791, when Haydn was awarded the degree of Doctor of Music by Oxford University.

THE "SURPRISE" SYMPHONY   Page 35

Haydn's first visit to London began on New Year's Day 1791, and was crowned with such success that he remained there until June, 1792. He visited the English metropolis to fulfill a contract with Johann Salomon, an orchestra conductor, to compose six symphonies and conduct them at the piano. The success of the first six was so great that Haydn wrote another series, one of which was the "Surprise" Symphony presented here. It was first played in London on March 23, 1792, and its nickname "Surprise" is derived from the fact that the *Andante* contains an extraordinarily loud drum beat at the conclusion of the first *pianissimo* presentation of the principal theme.

THE "SALOMON" SYMPHONY Page 51

This is another of the symphonies composed by Haydn during the visits made to London from 1791 to 1795. The remuneration for these symphonies was as follows: he received $1500 for six symphonies and $1000 for the copyright; $1000 for twenty new compositions to be produced at the same number of concerts, and $1000 guaranteed as the proceeds of a benefit concert. In comparison to the amounts received by Franz Schubert, these figures are apparently very substantial, but it must be remembered that Haydn had to pay all his own traveling expenses and his living expenses while in London.

THE "MILITARY" SYMPHONY Page 68

Haydn's second visit to London began on February 4, 1794, and ended on August 15, 1795; it is said that on the two visits he made a net profit of about $12,000, sufficient to relieve him of all anxiety of a financial character. The "Military" symphony was one of six written for the second English visit. It was performed in the Spring of 1794, and the nickname is derived from certain characteristics of its second movement such as the employment of several percussion instruments, and the use of an Austrian bugle call in the Coda. It is said that this symphony pleased the King so greatly, in spite of his previously expressed preference for the works of Handel, that Haydn was specially presented to his Majesty by the Prince of Wales.

THE "CLOCK" SYMPHONY Page 90

Sir George Grove reports that Haydn himself made the statement that it was not until after his visits to England that he became famous in Germany and Austria. Although this may not be strictly true, it is an undisputed fact that the English people were the first to give him not only recognition of the most flattering character, but also really substantial remuneration. The "Clock" symphony was one of twelve composed for the Salomon concerts in London, and was first performed at the Haymarket Theatre on May 4, 1795. It owes the nickname to the accompaniment figure used in the *Andante* movement, resembling the rhythmic tick-tack of a clock.

THE "LONDON" SYMPHONY Page 106

This symphony is one of the series written by Haydn during his second sojourn in England in 1795; it was first performed at one of the Opera Concerts in London, its nickname being derived naturally in remembrance of this occasion. J. Cuthbert Hadden, in his biography of Haydn, has this to say of the Salomon symphonies: "These, so far as his instrumental music is concerned, are the crowning glory of his life work. They are the ripe fruits of his long experience working upon the example of Mozart, and mark to the full all those qualities of natural geniality, humour, vigor and simple good-heartedness which are the leading characteristics of his style".

"Farewell" Symphony

Allegro assai EXPOSITION

Joseph Haydn
1732-1809

PRINCIPAL THEME

BRIDGE PASSAGE

DEVELOPMENT—SECTION I ∿∿∿

SUBORDINATE THEME ∿∿∿

CONCLUDING THEME (CO-

DEVELOPMENT—SECTION 2 ∿∿∿

DETTA) ∿∿∿

EXPOSITION
Adagio

DEVELOPMENT

DEVELOPMENT—SECTION 3 〰〰

RETURNING PASSAGE (RETRANSITION) 〰〰

RECAPITULATION

RETURN PRINCIPAL THEME 〰〰

BRIDGE PASSAGE 〰〰

RETURN SUBORDINATE THEME 〰〰

RETURN CONCLUDING THEME (CODETTA) 〰

PRINCIPAL SECTION
Menuetto
Allegretto

Oboi

Corni in Fis

Violino I

Violino II

Viola

Violoncello e Basso

PRINCIPAL THEME—PART I 〰〰

PRINCIPAL THEME—PART II 〰〰

(13)

CONCLUDING THEME (CODETTA) 〰〰〰〰〰〰〰〰〰〰〰

RETURNING PASSAGE (RETRANSITION) 〰〰〰〰

DEVELOPMENT

DEVELOPMENT—SECTION 1 〰〰〰〰

DEVELOPMENT—SECTION 2 〰〰〰〰

CODA
Adagio

SPECIAL CODA THEME—PART I ~~~~~~~~~

1st CONCLUDING THEME (CODETTA) ~~~~~~~~~

SPECIAL CODA

SPECIAL CODA THEME—

THEME—PART II ~~~~~~~~~

PART III ~~~~~~~~~

1st RETURN SPECIAL CODA THEME—

PART I

BRIDGE PASSAGE

2nd RETURN SPECIAL CODA THEME—PART I

2nd CONCLUD-

ING THEME (CODETTA)

"Oxford" Symphony

Joseph Haydn
(1732 – 1809)

SUBORDINATE THEME ∿∿∿

CONCLUDING THEME (CODETTA) ∿∿∿∿∿∿∿

(20)

RETURN SUBORDINATE THEME ~~~~~~~~~~

RETURN CONCLUDING THEME (CODETTA) ~~~~~~~~~~

CODA

(23)

BRIDGE PASSAGE

PRINCIPAL THEME—PART II

SUBORDINATE THEME

BRIDGE PASSAGE 〰〰〰〰

SUBORDINATE THEME 〰〰〰〰

CON-

CLUDING THEME (CODETTA)

DEVELOPMENT

DEVELOPMENT—SECTION I

DEVELOPMENT—SECTION 2

RETURNING PASSAGE (RETRAN-

DEVELOPMENT—SECTION 3 〰〰〰

SITION) 〰〰〰

54

56

RECAPITULATION

RETURN PRINCIPAL THEME—PART I 〰〰〰〰〰〰〰〰〰

RETURN PRIN-

CODA—SECTION 2

"Surprise" Symphony

Joseph Haydn
1732–1809

DEVELOPMENT

DEVELOPMENT—SECTION I 〰〰〰

CONCLUDING THEME (CO—

DETTA)—PART II 〰〰〰〰

DEVELOPMENT—

SECTION 2 〰〰〰

SITION) RETURN PRINCIPAL THEME—PART I

RETURNING PASSAGE (RETRAN—

RETURN PRINCIPAL THEME—PART II

21

23

RETURN CONCLUDING THEME (CODETTA)—

220

PART II ~~~~~~

22

230

RETURN CONCLUDING THEME (CODETTA)—PART I ~~~~

24

VARIATION FORM
Andante

Flauti	
Oboi	
Fagotti	
Corni in C	
Trombe in C	
Timpani in C-G	
Violino I	
Violino II	
Viola	
Violoncello e Basso	

THEME—PART I ~~~~~~

(40)

(43)

PRINCIPAL THEME—PART II, 1st

PRIN—

PART III

CONCLUDING

CIPAL THEME—PART II, 2nd PERIOD

BRIDGE PASSAGE

PRINCIPAL THEME

THEME (CODETTA)

Trio

SUBORDINATE THEME—PART I

SUBORDINATE THEME—PART II

SUBORDINATE THEME—PART III

Mon. D.C.

Allegro di molto RONDO FORM

Flauti
Oboi
Fagotti
Corni in G
Trombe in C
Timpani in D-G
Violino I
Violino II
Viola
Violoncello e Basso

PRINCIPAL THEME—PART I

PRINCIPAL THEME—PART II

PRINCIPAL—

THEME—PART III

BRIDGE PASSAGE

RETURN —

ING PASSAGE (RETRANSITION)　RETURN PRINCIPAL THEME—PART I 〰〰〰〰

2nd SUBORDINATE THEME 〰〰〰〰

BRIDGE PASSAGE 〰〰〰

BRIDGE PASSAGE 〰〰〰

RETURN PRINCIPAL THEME—PART I 〰〰〰〰〰〰

IFIED 〰〰〰〰〰〰〰〰

RETURN 2nd SUBORDINATE THEME MOD—

RETURN PRINCIPAL THEME

PART I 〰〰〰〰〰〰〰〰〰〰〰〰〰 RETURN—

PRINCIPAL THEME—PART II 〰〰〰〰〰

57

RETURN 1st SUBOR-

DINATE THEME ∿∿∿∿∿∿∿∿∿∿∿∿∿∿∿∿∿∿∿∿∿∿

58

210

RETURN CONCLUDING THEME (CODETTA) ∿∿∿

220   59

CODA

CODA—SECTION 1 ∿∿∿

60

CODA—SECTION 2 ∿∿∿

240

COLA—SECTION 3

260

Symphony Nº 7
(Salomon)

Joseph Haydn
1732-1809

BRIDGE PASSAGE ∿∿∿

SUBORDINATE THEME—PART I ∿∿∿∿∿∿

∿∿∿∿∿∿ SUBORDINATE THEME—PART II ∿∿∿∿∿

RECAPITULATION

RETURN PRINCIPAL THEME—PART I ᨊᨊᨊ

BRIDGE PASSAGE ᨊᨊᨊ

(55)

CODA—SECTION 2

VARIATION FORM
Adagio ma non troppo

PRINCIPAL THEME—PART I

PRINCIPAL THEME—PART II

CUT IN RECORD TO
LAST MEASURE P. 26

VARIATION I

END OF CUT

END OF CUT

CODA

CODA—SECTION I

Menuetto
Allegretto **PRINCIPAL SECTION**

Flauti
Oboi
Fagotti
Corni in C
Trombe in C
Timpani in C-G
Violino I
Violino II
Viola
Violoncello e Basso

PRINCIPAL THEME—PART I

CODA—SECTION 2

PRINCIPAL THEME—PART II

PRINCIPAL THEME—PART III

SUBORDINATE THEME—PART I

CONCLUDING THEME (CODETTA) ~~~~~

DEVELOPMENT

DEVELOPMENT—SECTION 1 ~~~~~

DEVELOPMENT—SECTION 2 ~~~~~

DEVELOPMENT—SECTION 3 ~~~~~

CODA—SECTION 1

CODA—SECTION 2

CODA—SECTION 3

CODA—SECTION 4

CODA—SECTION 5

"Military" Symphony

Joseph Haydn
1732-1809

PRINCIPAL THEME—PART II

BRIDGE PASSAGE

SUBORDINATE THEME—PART I

SUBORDINATE THEME—PART II

CONCLUDING THEME (CODETTA)

DEVELOPMENT—SECTION 2 ∿∿∿

RECAPITULATION

RETURN PRINCIPAL THEME—PART I ∿∿∿∿

RETURNING PASSAGE (RETRANSITION) ∿∿∿

BRIDGE PASSAGE ∿

RETURN SUBORDINATE THEME—PART II

CODA

CODA—SECTION I

CODA—SECTION 2

(73)

PRINCIPAL THEME—PART I REPEATED

PRINCIPAL THEME—

PART II REPEATED

PRINCIPAL THEME—

PRINCIPAL THEME—PART III RE-

PART II

PRINCIPAL THEME—PART III

TRIO

PEATED

SUBORDINATE THEME—

PART I

SUBORDINATE THEME—PART II

SUBORDINATE THEME—PART II REPEATED

RETURN PRINCIPAL THEME—PART II

RETURN PRINCIPAL SECTION

RETURN PRINCIPAL THEME—PART I

RETURN PRINCIPAL THEME—PART III

CODA

CODA—SECTION 1

CODA—SECTION 3 ～～～～

130

CODA—SECTION 2 ～～～～

140

CODA—SECTION 4 〰〰〰

CODA—SECTION 5 〰〰〰

49

180

CODA—SECTION 6 〰〰〰

51

MENUETTO. **PRINCIPAL SECTION**
Moderato.

Flauto.
Oboi.
Fagotti.
Corni in G.
Trombe in C.
Timpani in G. D.
Violino I.
Violino II.
Viola.
Violoncello Contrabasso

PRINCIPAL THEME—PART I 〰〰〰〰〰〰〰

50

52

20

PRINCIPAL THEME—PART II 〰〰〰〰〰〰〰〰〰〰〰

53

55

PRINCIPAL THEME—PART III

SUBORDINATE THEME—PART I

SUBORDINATE THEME—PART II

(81)

SUBORDINATE THEME —

PART III 〰〰〰〰〰〰〰〰〰〰〰〰〰〰〰〰〰〰

EXPOSITION
FINALE.
Presto.

PRINCIPAL THEME—PART I 〰〰〰〰〰〰〰〰

PRINCIPAL THEME—PART II 1st PERIOD

PART II 2nd PERIOD

PRINCIPAL THEME—PART II, 2nd PERIOD 〰〰〰〰

PRINCIPAL THEME—PART III

SUBORDINATE

BRIDGE

THEME—PART I

PASSAGE

SUBORDINATE THEME—PART II ∿∿∿∿∿

ING THEME (CODETTA) ∿∿∿∿∿

DEVELOPMENT

DEVELOPMENT—SECTION I ∿∿∿ DEVELOP-

CONCLUD ◄

MENT—SECTION 2 ∿∿∿

DEVELOPMENT—

DEVELOPMENT—SECTION 4

SECTION 3

DEVELOPMENT—SECTION 5

THEME—PART I

RETURNING PASSAGE (RETRAN-

74

SITION)

RECAPITULATION

RETURN PRINCIPAL

RETURN SUBORDINATE THEME—PART I

THEME—PART II 〰〰〰〰〰〰〰〰〰〰〰

RETURN SUBORDINATE

CODA—SECTION 2 〰〰〰

CODA—SECTION 1 〰〰〰

CODA—SECTION 3 〰〰〰

"Clock" Symphony

Joseph Haydn.
1732-1809.

RETURN PRINCIPAL THEME—PART II

BRIDGE PASSAGE

RE-

CAPITULATION

TURNING PRINCIPAL THEME—PART I

RETURN SUBORDINATE THEME

II.

SONG FORM
Andante.

CODA—SECTION 2

CODA—SECTION 3

PRINCIPAL THEME—PART I

PRINCIPAL THEME—PART II

PRINCIPAL THEME—PART III

VARIATION PRINCIPAL THEME—PART II

150

160

Men. D. C.

zu 2

30

zu 2

BRIDGE PASSAGE ~~~~~

RONDO FORM
IV.
Finale. Vivace.

Flauti.

Oboi.

Clarinetti in A.

Fagotti.

Corni in D.

Trombe in D.

Timpani in D-A.

Violino I.

Violino II.

Viola.

Violoncello e
Contrabasso.

PRINCIPAL THEME—PART I ~~~~~

Bassi

10

Vl.

Vla.

Vlc. e
Cb.

Vlc.

Bassi

Cb.

Vlc.

PRINCIPAL THEME—PART II ~~~~~

20

1.

Vl.

Vla.

Vlc. e
Cb.

Vlc.

~~~~~ PRINCIPAL THEME—PART III ~~~~~

10

50

zu 2

zu 2

RETURN PRINCIPAL THEME—PART I

RETURN PRINCIPAL THEME—PART II

BRIDGE PASSAGE

RETURN PRINCIPAL THEME IN FUGAL FORM ～～～

(104)

"London" Symphony

Joseph Haydn
1732-1809

CONCLUDING THEME (CODETTA)—PART I 〰

DEVELOPMENT

DEVELOPMENT—SECTION I 〰〰〰

CONCLUDING THEME (CODETTA)—PART II 〰〰〰

DEVELOPMENT—SECTION 2 〰〰〰

DEVELOPMENT—

SECTION 3 〰〰〰

DEVELOP ▬

MENT—SECTION 4 〰〰〰

RETURNING PASSAGE (RETRANSITION) 〰〰〰

RECAPITULATION

RETURN PRINCIPAL THEME—PART I, 1st PERIOD 〰〰〰〰〰

RETURN SUBORDINATE THEME—PART I

RETURN CONCLUDING THEME (CODETTA)—PART I

CODA—SECTION 2

CODA

CODA—SECTION I

PRINCIPAL THEME—PART III, 1st PERIOD

PRINCIPAL THEME—PART III, 2nd PERIOD

CONCLUDING THEME (CODETTA)

RONDO FORM
II
Andante

PRINCIPAL THEME—PART I

PRINCIPAL THEME—PART II

SUBORDINATE THEME— INTRODUCTION   SUBORDINATE THEME—PART I

RETURN PRINCIPAL THEME—PART III

RETURN PRINCIPAL THEME—

PART II

PRINCIPAL THEME—PART III REPEATED

CLUDING THEME (CODETTA)

RETURN CON-

III

Menuetto Allegro **PRINCIPAL SECTION**

Flauti
Oboi
Clarinetti in A
Fagotti
Corni in D
Trombe in D
Timpani in D-A
Violino I
Violino II
Viola
Violoncello e Contrabasso

PRINCIPAL THEME—PART I

PRINCIPAL THEME—PART II, 1st PERIOD 〰〰〰〰〰〰〰〰〰〰

PRINCIPAL THEME—PART II, 2nd PERIOD 〰〰〰〰〰〰〰〰〰

TRIO

SUBORDINATE THEME—PART I 〰〰〰〰〰〰〰〰

PRIN~

CIPAL THEME—PART III 〰〰〰〰〰〰〰〰〰〰

SUBORDINATE THEME—PART II 〰〰〰〰〰〰〰〰

SUBORDINATE THEME—PART III 〰〰〰〰〰

BRIDGE PASSAGE 〰〰〰   *Men. D.C.*

PRINCIPAL THEME—PART II 〰〰〰〰〰〰〰〰

IV

Allegro spiritoso EXPOSITION

Flauti
Oboi
Clarinetti in A
Fagotti
Corni in D
Trombe in D
Timpani in D-A
Violino I
Violino II
Viola
Violoncello
Contrabasso

PRINCIPAL THEME—PART I 〰〰〰〰〰〰

(117)

49

51
60

BRIDGE PASSAGE 〰〰〰

SUBORDINATE THEME—PART I 〰〰〰

50
40
50

52

SUBORDINATE THEME—

70

PART II, 1st PERIOD 〰〰〰〰〰〰〰〰〰〰〰

SUBORDINATE THEME—PART II, 2nd PERIOD 〰〰〰〰〰〰

CONCLUDING THEME (CODETTA)—PART I 〰〰〰

SUBORDINATE THEME—PART III 〰〰〰〰〰〰

CONCLUDING THEME (CODETTA)—PART II

DEVELOPMENT

DEVELOPMENT—SECTION I

DEVELOPMENT—SECTION 2 〰〰

DEVELOPMENT—SECTION 3 〰〰

CONCLUDING

PASSAGE (RETRANSITION)

190

RECAPITULATION

200

RETURN PRINCIPAL THEME—PART I

210

RETURN PRINCIPAL THEME—PART II

210

220

RETURN SUBORDINATE

THEME—PART I   RETURN SUBORDINATE

RETURN SUBORDINATE THEME—PART II, 2nd PERIOD

RETURN SUBORDINATE THEME—PART III ∿∿∿∿

THEME—PART II, 1st PERIOD ∿∿∿∿

CODA

CODA—SECTION I ∿∿∿

HISTORICAL AND CRITICAL COMMENT ON MOZART SYMPHONIES

The symphonies of Wolfgang Amadeus Mozart were scored for the following instruments:

Flauti (Flutes)	*Fl.*	Timpani	*Timp.*
Oboi (Oboes)	*Ob.*	Violini (Violins)	*Vl.*
Clarinetti (Clarinets)	*Cl.*	Viola	*Vla.*
Fagotti (Bassoons)	*Fg.*	Violoncello	*Vc.*
Corni (Horns)	*Cor.*	Contrabasso (Basso)	*Cb. or B.*
Trombe (Trumpets)	*Tbe.*		

These are the names under which the instruments are listed on the first page of each score; the abbreviation used on succeeding pages follows. No trombones are used in any of the Mozart symphonies.

THE "HAFFNER" SYMPHONY   Köchel Catalogue No. 385   Page 128

This symphony was written for some festive occasion in the house of Siegmund Haffner, the Mayor of Salzburg; six years previously, Mozart had composed the famous "Serenade" which was played when Haffner's daughter, Elizabeth, was married. The symphony was also originally intended as a serenade; in this form it had an introductory march and two minuets which Mozart eliminated in 1783, transforming the work into a four-movement symphony. It is said that, having composed the work at top speed, Mozart forgot all about it so that upon the return of the manuscript, he was agreeably surprised at its excellence. Critics are agreed that the symphony clearly manifests the influence of Josef Haydn; it would also appear that certain themes resemble airs to be found in Mozart's musical comedy "Die Entführung aus dem Serail" which was also composed in 1782.

THE "LINZ" SYMPHONY   Köchel Catalogue No. 425   Page 146

Mozart completed this symphony at Linz on November 3, 1783, and it was first performed at a concert in the same city the following day; hence its nickname. Just as Beethoven's first symphonies give evidence of his admiration for both Haydn and Mozart, in the same way this symphony manifests Mozart's deep veneration for Haydn, but his own individual style is clearly evident both in its construction and its instrumentation. Such innovations appear as the use of the trumpets in the slow movement, and the introduction of a subordinate theme in the same movement which overshadows the principal theme in importance. Another distinct departure from the Haydn tradition is the elaborate development period in both the first and last movements. It is interesting to note that the Principal Theme and the Subordinate Theme in the first movement are so much alike that unless one listens closely they appear to be exactly the same.

THE "PRAGUE" SYMPHONY   KÖCHEL CATALOGUE No. 504   Page 162

This work is also known as the *Symphony without a Minuet* because it consists of only three movements, like many of the earliest symphonies. In musical value it not only compares favorably with the three great symphonies composed in the last year of Mozart's life, but it actually surpasses them in respect to conciseness and plasticity in form. The work was written at Vienna in 1786, and had its first performance during January, 1787; at that time Mozart was enjoying the tremendous success of his opera "The Marriage of Figaro" at Prague. The symphony was played in a concert given at the opera-house; some concerted works followed, and then Mozart, seating himself at the clavier, in response to tumultuous applause, extemporized twelve marvellously brilliant and extremely difficult variations on the theme from the song *Non piu andrai* from "Figaro."

SYMPHONY IN Eb MAJOR   KÖCHEL CATALOGUE No. 543   Page 180

Mozart composed his three greatest symphonies during the summer of 1788; they were completed in less than nine weeks. The first was the Symphony in Eb Major, finished on June 26; the second was the Symphony in G Minor, completed in July; the third was the "Jupiter" Symphony completed on August 10. It is very interesting to note that while Mozart could dash off a piece of chamber music or a concerto for some intimate friend in a few hours, he looked upon his symphonic writing from a much more serious standpoint, and always spent no little time in revising or polishing the instrumentation. It may be true that he was the greatest melodist among the classic composers; it is equally true that his intuitive sense of proportion has rendered his symphonies architectural monuments from the standpoint of design.

SYMPHONY IN G MINOR   KÖCHEL CATALOGUE No. 550   Page 196

The earliest symphonies by Philipp Emanuel Bach, Gossec, Dittersdorf and Boccherini employed only the instruments of the string quartet, the double-bass, two oboes and two horns. Even Haydn's earlier symphonies had only this instrumentation; later the Austrian master added the flute, the bassoon, the trumpet and the kettle-drums—the clarinet was also used by him at times. Mozart employed this later instrumentation, but only utilized the clarinet in his more mature works after having heard the instrument and become greatly enamoured of its tone qualities. Neither Haydn nor Mozart used the trombone; it was first introduced by Beethoven and Schubert. The G Minor Symphony employed no clarinets in its original autograph score; a later revision by the composer added clarinet parts, and also made some changes in the oboe part. This is the version of which the score is used in this volume.

A few words of information about Dr. Ludwig Köchel will have its interest at this point. Köchel was a learned musician whose name is now immortal through a chronological thematic catalogue which he compiled of all Mozart's works, assigning each work a number (in the instance of this symphony No. 551), and adding to it a list of compositions which have been lost or were doubtful in origin. He also aided in the preparation of the complete edition of Mozart's works published by Breitkopf and Härtel, and was an intimate friend of Otto Jahn, author of an important biography of Mozart.

This symphony was the last of three written by Mozart in 1788; the composer is not responsible for the subtitle "Jupiter" which is probably an appellation bestowed by some ardent admirer of the work. The *Andante* is regarded as not only one of the most impressive slow movements conceived by Mozart but also as a striking example of classic beauty in symphonic composition.

The *Finale* of this symphony is one of the most remarkable examples of contrapuntal writing in all symphonic literature, whether it be classic or modern. Five themes, selected from the material used in this movement, are combined together in the *Coda*, revealing an extraordinary fugal exposition in quintuple counterpoint. It constitutes a unique example of the magnificent effects which can be secured by combining the severest of musical forms with inspired thematic material.

"Haffner" Symphony

BRIDGE PASSAGE 〰〰〰

_f_ SUBORDINATE

THEME—PART I 〰〰〰〰〰〰〰〰〰〰〰〰〰〰〰〰〰〰〰〰〰〰〰

SUBORDINATE THEME—PART II 〰〰〰〰〰〰〰〰〰〰〰

SUBORDINATE THEME—PART III 〰〰

CONCLUDING THEME (CODETTA)—PART I ⌇⌇⌇⌇⌇⌇⌇⌇⌇⌇⌇⌇

CONCLUDING THEME

(CODETTA)—PART II ⌇⌇⌇⌇⌇⌇⌇⌇⌇⌇⌇⌇⌇⌇⌇⌇⌇⌇⌇⌇

13

14

CONCLUDING THEME (CODETTA)—PART III ∿∿∿∿

15

DEVELOPMENT

DEVELOPMENT—SECTION I ∿∿∿∿

16

DEVELOPMENT—SECTION 2 〜〜〜〜

Fugato
starts

RECAPITULATION   RETURNING PASSAGE (RETRANSITION) 〜〜〜

RETURN PRINCIPAL THEME—PART I 〜〜〜〜〜〜〜〜〜〜〜〜〜〜〜〜

RETURN SUBORDINATE THEME—PART II 〜〜〜〜〜

RETURN SUBOR-

DINATE THEME—PART III

RETURN CONCLUDING THEME (CODETTA)—PART I

RETURN CONCLUDING THEME

(CODETTA)—PART II

RETURN CONCLUDING THEME

(CODETTA)—PART III

EXPOSITION **II**

PRINCIPAL THEME

SUBORDINATE THEME

DEVELOPMENT—SECTION 1

DEVELOPMENT—SECTION 2

CONCLUDING THEME (CODETTA)

RETURNING PASSAGE (RETRANSITION)

RECAPITULATION

RETURN PRINCIPAL THEME

RETURN SUBORDINATE THEME 〰〰〰〰〰〰〰〰〰〰〰〰〰〰〰

RETURN CONCLUDING THEME (CODETTA) 〰〰

(137)

BRIDGE PASSAGE 〰〰〰

SUBORDINATE THEME—PART II 〰〰〰〰〰〰〰〰〰

CONCLUDING THEME (CODETTA)—PART I 〰〰〰〰〰

SUBORDI—

NATE THEME—PART I 〰〰〰〰〰〰〰〰〰〰〰〰〰

CONCLUDING THEME (CODETTA)—PART II   BRIDGE PASSAGE ~~~~~~ DEVELOPMENT

DEVELOPMENT—SECTION

DEVELOPMENT—SECTION 2 ~~~~~~

THEME—PART I, 1st PERIOD ∿∿∿∿∿∿∿∿∿∿∿∿

RETURN PRINCIPAL THEME—PART I, 2nd PERIOD ∿∿∿∿∿∿

RETURNING

PASSAGE (RETRANSITION) ∿∿∿∿∿

RECAPITULATION

RETURN PRINCIPAL

RETURN PRINCIPAL THEME—PART II 〰〰〰〰〰

RETURN SUBORDINATE THEME—PART I 〰〰〰〰〰〰〰〰〰〰〰〰〰〰

RETURN SUBORDINATE THEME—PART II

RETURN CONCLUDING THEME (CODETTA)—PART I

RETURN

CODA

CONCLUDING THEME (CODETTA)—PART II   CODA—SECTION I

Magic Modulation

CODA—SECTION 2

CODA—SECTION 3 ~~~~~

"Linz" Symphony

W. A. Mozart.
1756-1791.

DEVELOPMENT—SECTION 2 〜〜〜

RETURNING

RECAPITULATION

PASSAGE (RETRANSITION) 〜 RETURN PRINCIPAL THEME—PART I 〜〜〜

RETURN PRINCIPAL THEME—PART II 〜〜〜

II.

Poco Adagio. **EXPOSITION**

IV.

RETURN CONCLUDING THEME (CODETTA) ∿

"Prague" Symphony

W. A. Mozart
(1756-1791)

BRIDGE PASSAGE 〰

EXPOSITION
Allegro

PRINCIPAL THEME—PART I 〰〰〰〰〰

PRINCIPAL THEME—PART II 〰〰〰〰〰

BRIDGE PASSAGE

combination of motives in diff ways

A' V

A²

CONCLUDING THEME (CODETTA)—PART III ⩘⩘⩘⩘⩘

CONCLUDING THEME (CODETTA)—PART IV

DEVELOPMENT

DEVELOPMENT—SECTION I ⩘⩘⩘⩘⩘

imitative combine w/ counterpoint var, verds

DEVELOPMENT—SEC-
(A₂)

TION 2 ⩘⩘⩘⩘

DEVELOPMENT—SECTION 3

RETURNING PASSAGE (RETRANSITION)

(167)

RECAPITULATION

RETURN PRINCIPAL THEME—PART I ∿

BRIDGE PASSAGE ∿

SUBORDINATE THEME 〰〰〰〰〰〰

CONCLUDING THEME (CODETTA) 〰〰〰〰〰〰

DEVELOPMENT

DEVELOPMENT—SECTION 1 〰〰〰

DEVELOPMENT—SECTION 2 〰

225

BRIDGE PASSAGE

235

240

245

250

255

260

RETURN SUBORDINATE THEME—PART I

265

270

280

285

RETURN SUBORDINATE THEME—PART II

THEME (CODETTA)—PART II

RETURN CONCLUDING THEME (CODETTA)—PART I

RETURN CONCLUDING

RETURN CONCLUDING THEME (CODETTA)—PART III

Symphony in Eb Major

PRINCIPAL THEME—PART I

BRIDGE PASSAGE

PRINCIPAL THEME—PART II

DEVELOPMENT

RETURN PRINCIPAL THEME—PART II ⌇⌇⌇⌇⌇⌇⌇⌇

BRIDGE PASSAGE ⌇⌇⌇⌇⌇⌇⌇⌇

21

ORDINATE THEME—PART I

RETURN SUB-

22

RETURN SUBORDINATE THEME—PART II

23

RETURN CONCLUDING THEME (CODETTA)—PART I

24

RETURN CONCLUDING

THEME (CODETTA)—PART II

CODA

PRINCIPAL

THEME—PART III

BRIDGE PASSAGE SUBORDINATE THEME—PART I

f minor "strong second
Theme"

EXPOSITION
Andante

Flauto
Clarinetti in B
Fagotti
Corni in Es
Violino I
Violino II
Viola
Violoncello
Basso

PRINCIPAL THEME—PART I

PRINCIPAL THEME—PART II

SUBORDINATE THEME—PART II

B²

RETURNING PASSAGE (RETRANSITION)   RETURN PRINCIPAL THEME—PART I

RETURN PRIN—

CONCLUDING THEME (CODETTA)

CIPAL THEME—PART II

RETURN PRINCIPAL THEME—PART III

BRIDGE PASSAGE **RETURN SUBORD—**

New enharmonic usage

Ab min → G# min Bb Maj
b min

RETURN SUBORDINATE

THEME—PART II

INATE THEME—PART I

Analyse

G⁰⁷ Ab min → Bb Maj

(188)

41

PRINCIPAL THEME—PART II

PRINCIPAL THEME—PART III

43

TRIO

SUBORDINATE THEME—PART I

SUBORDINATE THEME—PART II

42

Fine

THEME—PART III

44

SUBORDINATE

THEME—PART III

Menuetto D.C. al Fine.

CONCLUDING THEME

CONCLUDING

THEME (CODETTA)—PART I 〰〰〰〰〰〰〰〰〰〰

(CODETTA)—PART II 〰〰〰〰〰〰

DEVELOPMENT

DEVELOPMENT—SECTION I 〰〰

DEVELOPMENT—SECTION 2 〰〰

RETURNING PASSAGE (RETRANSITION) 〰〰

61

63

RETURN CONCLUDING THEME (CODETTA)—PART II

62

64

RETURN CONCLUDING THEME (CODETTA)—PART I

Symphony in G Minor

W.A.Mozart
1756-1791

CONCLUDING THEME (CODETTA)—PART I 〰️

CONCLUDING THEME (CODETTA)—PART II

CONCLUDING THEME (CODETTA)—PART III ∿∿∿∿

DEVELOPMENT

DEVELOPMENT—SECTION I ∿∿∿∿

DEVELOPMENT—SECTION 2 ∿∿

DEVELOPMENT—SECTION 3

RECAPITULATION

RETURN PRINCIPAL THEME—PART I, 1st PERIOD

RETURN PRINCIPAL

RETURNING PASSAGE (RETRANSITION)

THEME—PART I, 2nd PERIOD

(199)

190

210

220

RETURN PRINCIPAL THEME—PART II ∿∿∿∿∿∿∿∿∿∿∿

BRIDGE PASSAGE ∿∿∿∿

200

230

RETURN SUBORDINATE THEME ∿∿∿∿∿∿∿∿∿∿∿∿∿∿

RETURN

CONCLUDING THEME (CODETTA)—PART I ∿∿∿∿∿∿∿∿∿∿∿

29

31

BRIDGE PASSAGE

CONCLUDING THEME (CODETTA)

30

32

SUBORDINATE THEME

DEVELOPMENT

DEVELOPMENT—SECTION I

(203)

RETURN PRINCIPAL THEME—PART I, 1st PERIOD 〰〰〰〰

RETURN PRINCIPAL THEME—PART I, 2nd PERIOD

RETURN PRINCIPAL THEME—PART II 〰〰〰

DEVELOPMENT—SECTION 2 〰〰〰

RETURNING

PASSAGE (RETRANSITION) 〰〰〰

BRIDGE PASSAGE 〰〰〰

PRINCIPAL THEME—PART II

PRINCIPAL

TRIO

SUBORDINATE THEME—PART I

THEME—PART III

CONCLUDING THEME (CODETTA) [Fine]

SUBORDINATE THEME—PART II

SUBORDINATE THEME—PART III

CONCLUDING THEME (CODETTA) D.C. Menuetto

EXPOSITION IV
[Finale]. Allegro assai

PRINCIPAL THEME—PART I, 1st PERIOD

PRINCIPAL THEME—PART I, 2nd PERIOD

PRINCIPAL THEME—PART II

BRIDGE PASSAGE

CONCLUDING THEME

(CODETTA)—PART II ~~~~~~~~~~~~~~~~

DEVELOPMENT

DEVELOPMENT—SECTION I ~~~~~

DEVELOPMENT—SECTION 2 ~~~~~

DEVELOPMENT—SECTION 3 ~~~~~

DEVELOPMENT—SECTION 4 〰〰〰

RETURNING PASSAGE (RETRANSITION) 〰〰〰

RECAPITULATION

RETURN PRINCIPAL THEME—PART I, 1st PERIOD

RETURN PRINCIPAL THEME—PART I,

2nd PERIOD 〰〰〰〰〰〰〰〰 RETURN PRINCIPAL THEME—

-PART II 〰〰〰〰〰〰〰〰〰〰〰〰〰 BRIDGE PASSAGE

RETURN SUBORDINATE THEME

RETURN CONCLUDING THEME (CODETTA)—PART I

CONCLUDING THEME (CODETTA)—PART II ~~~~~~~~~~~~

"Jupiter" Symphony

W. A. Mozart
1756-1791

PRINCIPAL THEME—PART I, 1st PERIOD

PRINCIPAL THEME—PART I, 2nd PERIOD

PRINCIPAL THEME—PART I, 3rd PERIOD

BRIDGE PASSAGE

SUBORDINATE THEME—PART I, 1st PERIOD 〰〰

SUBORDINATE THEME—PART I,

2nd PERIOD 〰〰〰

SUBORDINATE THEME—PART II

CONCLUDING THEME (CODETTA)—PART I 〰〰〰

CONCLUDING THEME (CODETTA)—PART II

CONCLUDING THEME (CODETTA)—PART IV

DEVELOPMENT

DEVELOPMENT—SECTION 1

CONCLUDING THEME (CODETTA)—PART III

DEVELOPMENT—SECTION 2

15

DEVELOPMENT—SECTION 4

14

16

DEVELOPMENT—SECTION 3 ∿∿∿

DEVELOPMENT—SECTION 5 ∿∿∿

RETURNING PASSAGE (RETRANSITION) ᵕᵕᵕᵕᵕ

[poco rit.] [**RECAPITULATION**

RETURN PRINCIPAL THEME—PART I, 1st PERIOD ᵕᵕᵕᵕᵕ

RETURN PRINCIPAL THEME—PART I, 2nd PERIOD ᵕᵕᵕᵕᵕᵕᵕᵕ

RETURN CONCLUDING THEME (CODETTA)—PART II

RETURN CONCLUDING THEME (CODETTA)—PART I

RETURN CONCLUDING THEME (CODETTA)—

PART III

PASSAGE

SUBORDINATE THEME

CONCLUDING THEME (CO-

DETTA)

34

36

DEVELOPMENT

DEVELOPMENT—SECTION I

RETURNING PASSAGE (RETRANSITION) ∿∿∿

RECAPITULATION

RETURN PRINCIPAL THEME—PART I (MODIFIED) ∿∿∿

BRIDGE PASSAGE ∿∿∿

RETURN SUBORDINATE THEME ∿∿∿∿∿∿

RETURN CONCLUDING THEME (CODETTA)∿∿∿∿

CODA

CODA—SECTION I

ING THEME (CODETTA)—PART I ~~~~~~~~~~~~~~~~~~~ CONCLUDING

THEME (CODETTA)—PART II ~~~~~~~~~~~~~~~~~~~

SUBORD—

INATE THEME—PART III ~~~~~~~~~~~~~ [Menuetto D.C. al Fine.]

TRIO

SUBORDINATE THEME—PART I ~~~~~~~~~~~~~

SUBORDINATE THEME—PART II ~~~~~~~~~~~~~

EXPOSITION   IV

Molto Allegro

Flauto
2 Oboi
2 Fagotti
2 Corni in C
2 Trombe in C
Timpani in C-G
Violino I
Violino II
Viola
Violoncello e Basso

PRINCIPAL THEME—PART I ~~~~~~~~~~~~~

PRINCIPAL THEME—PART II ∿∿∿∿∿

PRINCIPAL THEME—PART III ∿∿∿∿∿

BRIDGE PASSAGE ∿∿∿∿

DEVELOPMENT—SECTION 2 〰〰

DEVELOPMENT—SECTION 4 〰

DEVELOPMENT—SECTION 3

RETURNING PASSAGE (RETRANSITION) 〰〰〰

RECAPITULATION

RETURN PRINCIPAL THEME—PART I 〰〰〰〰〰〰〰

BRIDGE PASSAGE 〰〰〰〰〰

RETURN SUBORDINATE THEME—PART I 〰〰〰〰〰

HISTORICAL AND CRITICAL COMMENT ON
SCHUBERT SYMPHONIES

The symphonies of Franz Peter Schubert were scored for the following instruments:

Flauti or Flöten (Flutes)	*Fl.*
Oboi or Hoboen (Oboes)	*Ob. or Hb.*
Clarinetti or Klarinetten (Clarinets)	*Cl. or Kl.*
Fagotti or Fagotte (Bassoons)	*Fg.*
Corni or Hörner (Horns)	*Cor. or Hr.*
Trombe or Trompeten (Trumpets)	*Tbe. or Tr.*
Tromboni or Posaunen (Trombones)	*Tbni. or Pos.*
Timpani or Pauken (Tympani)	*Timp. or Pk.*
Violini (Violins)	*Vl.*
Violi or Bratschen (Violas)	*Vla. or Br.*
Violoncello or Violoncelli	*Vc.*
Contrabasso or Kontrabässe	*Cb. or Kb.*

These are the names under which the instruments are listed on the first page of each score; the abbreviation used on succeeding pages follows. Schubert uses the trombones in both the "Unfinished" and the C Major Symphonies.

THE "UNFINISHED" SYMPHONY Page 237

Schubert completed two movements of this symphony in October, 1822; the score was given to his friend, Anselm Hüttenbrenner, and not performed until December 17, 1865, at a concert given by a musical society in Vienna under the direction of Johann Herbeck. The symphony differs from all other Schubert works of this kind in that it is deeply tinged with romanticism, and really becomes a bridge between the works of the late classicists and the early romanticists. Both movements are written in polyphonic style, but the instrumentation is so unusual that Schubert becomes a pioneer in orchestral tone painting for everyone who studies this score closely.

Why Schubert did not complete this symphony is a question which up to the present time remains unanswered. The Gesellschaft der Musikfreunde of Vienna has in its possession what is apparently an unfinished sketch for the third movement (*Scherzo*) of this symphony. This fragment ends with the middle portion of the Trio. Apparently the instrumentation of nine measures were completed; these measures, and also the three piano manuscript pages are reproduced on Page 235.

SCHERZO FRAGMENT

This is a reproduction of the nine bars orchestrated for the Scherzo of the "Unfinished" Symphony by Franz Schubert.

This is the first page of the manuscript notes for the projected Scherzo.

2nd page of the piano manuscript.

3rd page of the piano manuscript.

The manuscript ends abruptly at this point.

SYMPHONY IN C MAJOR Page 253

This symphony was completed in March, 1828, and submitted to the Gesselschaft der Musikfreunde of Vienna for approval, rehearsal and public performance. Unfortunately, when rehearsal time came, members of the orchestra pronounced it not only too long but also too difficult, so all idea of performing it was dropped. Ten years later, Robert Schumann met Schubert's brother, Ferdinand, while on a visit to Vienna. The manuscript of the symphony, which was in Ferdinand's possession, was shown him and created a deep impression. He took it back to Leipzig, and the first performance took place on March 21, 1839, in the Leipzig Gewandhaus under Felix Mendelssohn, creating a most extraordinary impression on its hearers.

At that time Robert Schumann was the editor of the *Neue Zeitschrift Für Musik,* and his critical opinion of this symphony is well worth quoting from: "I say quite frankly that he who is not acquainted with this symphony knows but little of Schubert, though, in view of what the master has already given to the world, this may appear exaggerated praise. Herein is revealed the finest technical skill, life in every fibre of the music, the finest gradations of coloring and care for the minutest detail; the whole structure is shrouded in the cloak of romanticism which has now become familiar to us in Schubert's compositions. It has, too, the same heavenly length as, say, a four-volume novel by Jean Paul, who went on and on and never could come to an end. How gratifying to the ear is this wealth of invention in Schubert; and how we dread the coming to a close in the works of others, for fear of disappointment! . . . No symphony has made such a strong impression upon us since the days of Beethoven".

SYMPHONY IN B♭ MAJOR Page 320

Schubert started work on this symphony—which is called No. 5—in September, 1816, and completed it in October. The scoring is for a rather small orchestra—one flute, two oboes, two bassoons, two horns and the usual strings—there are no parts for clarinet, trumpet or drums.

Heinrich Kreissle von Hellborn, a devoted admirer of Schubert, who wrote both a biographical sketch and an exhaustive biography of the great Austrian composer, accounts for the omission of the clarinet, trumpet and drum parts by saying that the work was written for a circle of amateurs who used to hold orchestral practise at the home of Schubert's father, and that these two wind instruments and the drums were missing from the little ensemble. Its first performance was supposed to have been given at the home of Otto Hadwig, a member of one of the theatre orchestras, the performers being the little group of Schubert enthusiasts mentioned above by Kreissle.

Unfinished Symphony

PASSAGE ∿∿∿∿   SUBORDINATE THEME—PART I

BRIDGE

SUBORDINATE THEME—PART II

CONCLUDING THEME (CO-

OPMENT

OPMENT—SECTION I 〰〰〰〰〰〰〰〰 DEVELOPMENT—SECTION 2 〰〰

DEVELOPMENT—SECTION 3 〰〰〰〰

DEVEL-

DETTA) 〰〰〰〰〰〰〰〰〰

DEVEL-

DEVELOPMENT—SECTION 4

17

19

18

20

(241)

21

DEVELOPMENT—SECTION 7 〜〜〜〜

23

DEVELOPMENT—SECTION 8 〜〜〜〜

22

24

RETURNING PASSAGE (RETRANSITION) 〜〜〜〜

BRIDGE

RETURN SUBORDINATE THEME—PART II 〰〰〰

PASSAGE 〰〰 **RETURN SUBORDINATE THEME—PART I** 〰〰〰

33

35

CONCLUDING THEME (CODETTA) 〰〰〰〰

34

RETURN

36

CODA

CODA—SECTION 1   CODA—SECTION 2 〰

PRINCIPAL THEME—PART II

PRINCIPAL THEME—PART III

BRIDGE PASSAGE

(247)

SUBORDINATE THEME

SAGE (RETRANSITION) ~~~~~~

ULATION

RETURN PRINCIPAL THEME—PART I ~~~~~~

RETURNING PAS –

RETURN PRINCIPAL THEME—PART II ∿∿∿

PASSAGE ∿∿∿   RETURN SUBORDINATE THEME ∿∿∿

RETURN PRINCIPAL THEME—PART III ∿∿∿

BRIDGE

Symphony in C Major

I

Franz Schubert, Op. posth.
1797-1828

INTRODUCTION—PART V

PRINCIPAL THEME—PART I, 2nd PERIOD

EXPOSITION

Allegro ma non troppo

PRINCIPAL THEME—PART I, 1st PERIOD

PRINCIPAL THEME—PART II

BRIDGE PASSAGE 〰〰〰

SUBORDINATE THEME—PART I 〰〰〰

SUBORDINATE THEME—PART II 〰〰〰

CONCLUDING THEME

(CODETTA)—PART I 〰〰〰

CONCLUDING THEME (CODETTA)—PART II 〰〰〰

CONCLUDING THEME (CODETTA)—PART III

RETURNING PASSAGE (RETRANSITION) ∿∿∿

RECAPITULATION

RETURN PRINCIPAL

THEME—PART I, 1st PERIOD

RETURN PRINCIPAL THEME—PART I, 2nd PERIOD

RETURN PRINCIPAL THEME—PART II

53

55

54

56

440

450

460

BRIDGE PASSAGE decresc. RETURN SUBORD -

INATE THEME—PART I

(266)

RETURN SUBORDINATE THEME— PART II

(267)

RETURN CONCLUDING THEME (CODETTA)—

ING THEME (CODETTA)—PART II ⌇⌇⌇⌇

PART I ⌇⌇⌇⌇

RETURN CONCLUD-

RETURN CONCLUDING THEME (CODETTA)—PART III

RETURN CONCLUDING THEME (CODETTA)—PART IV

CODA
Più moto

CODA—SECTION I

CODA—SECTION 2 〰〰〰

CODA—REPETITION

OF SECTION 2

(272)

82

84

CODA—SECTION 3

CODA—SECTION 4

REPETITION PRINCIPAL THEME—PART III ∿∿∿

BRIDGE PASSAGE ∿∿∿ SUBORDINATE THEME—PART I ∿∿∿∿

SUBORD-

INATE THEME—PART II 〰〰〰〰〰〰〰〰〰〰〰〰〰 SUBORD—

INATE THEME—PART III 〰〰〰〰〰〰〰〰〰〰〰〰〰〰〰〰〰

RETURNING PASSAGE (RETRANSITION) 〰〰〰

RECAPITULATION

RETURN PRINCIPAL THEME—PART I,

101

103

102

104

105

1st PERIOD

RETURN PRINCIPAL THEME—PART I, 2nd

106

PERIOD

107

RETURN PRINCIPAL THEME—PART II

108

(279)

RÉPETITION OF PRINCIPAL THEME—

RETURN PRINCIPAL THEME—PART III

PART II

RETURN SUBORDINATE THEME—PART I 〰〰

RETURN SUBORDINATE THEME—PART II 〰〰

RETURN SUBORDINATE THEME—PART III

III. Scherzo

RETURN PRINCIPAL THEME—PART II

RECAPITULATION

f **RETURNING PASSAGE (RETRANSITION)**

RETURN PRINCIPAL THEME—PART I

RETURN SUBORDINATE THEME—PART I ∿∿∿

CODA—SECTION I ∿∿∿

RETURN SUBORDINATE THEME—PART II ∿∿∿

CODA—SECTION 2 ∿∿∿

PRINCIPAL THEME—PART I, 3rd PERIOD 〰〰〰

PRINCIPAL THEME—PART II, 2nd PERIOD 〰〰〰〰〰〰

PRINCIPAL THEME—PART II, 1st PERIOD 〰〰〰

〰〰 PRINCIPAL THEME—PART II, 3rd PERIOD 〰〰

PRINCIPAL THEME—PART III,

THEME—PART III, 1st PERIOD

PRINCIPAL

2nd PERIOD

(292)

RETURNING PASSAGE (RETRANSITION)

PRINCIPAL THEME—PART III.

IV. Finale

Allegro vivace **EXPOSITION**

2 Flauti
2 Oboi
2 Clarinetti in C
2 Fagotti
2 Corni in C
2 Trombe in C
3 Tromboni — Alto Tenore / Basso
Timpani in C-G
Violino — I / II
Viola
Violoncello
Contrabasso

PRINCIPAL THEME—PART I, 1st PERIOD

(293)

PRINCIPAL THEME—PART I, 2nd PERIOD

PRINCIPAL THEME—

-PART II, 1st PERIOD

PRINCIPAL THEME—PART II, 2nd

PERIOD ~~~~~ REPETITION PRINCIPAL THEME—PART II, 1st PERIOD

CONCLUDING THEME (CODETTA)

189

SUBORDINATE THEME—PART III, 4th PERIOD ∿∿∿∿∿∿∿∿∿

191

190

CONCLUDING THEME (CODETTA)—PART I ∿∿∿∿∿∿∿∿∿

192

REPETITION CONCLUDING THEME (CODETTA)—PART I ✍

DETTA)—PART II ~~~~~~

CONCLUDING THEME (CO-

CONCLUDING THEME (CODETTA)—PART III ~~~~~~

201

BRIDGE PASSAGE ∿ DEVELOPMENT—SECTION I ∿∿∿

203

OPMENT—SECTION I ∿∿∿

202

204

DEVELOPMENT—SECTION 2

DEVELOPMENT—SECTION 3

1st REPETITION OF DEVELOPMENT—SECTION 3

2nd REPETITION OF DEVEL—

OPMENT—SECTION 3

PART I, 1st PERIOD ∿∿∿∿∿∿∿∿∿∿

TRANSITION) ∿∿∿∿

RECAPITULATION

RETURN PRINCIPAL THEME—

RETURN PRIN—

CIPAL THEME—PART I, 2nd PERIOD 〰〰〰〰

RETURN PRINCIPAL THEME—PART II, 1st PERIOD 〰〰〰〰

RETURN CONCLUDING THEME (CODETTA)

RETURN PRINCIPAL THEME—PART II, 2nd PERIOD

BRIDGE

PASSAGE ～～～～～

RETURN SUBORDINATE THEME—PART II

PART II

RETURN SUBORDINATE THEME—PART III

RETURN CONCLUDING THEME (CODETTA)—PART I

REPETITION CONCLUDING

THEME (CODETTA)—PART I

RETURN CONCLUDING THEME (CODETTA)—PART II 〰〰

CODA

CODA—SECTION I 〰〰

RETURN CONCLUDING THEME (CODETTA)—PART III 〰〰

(316)

CODA—SECTION 3 〰〰〰

Symphony in B♭ Major

Franz Schubert
(1797 - 1828)

CONCLUDING THEME (CODETTA)—PART II 〰️

DEVELOPMENT—SECTION 2 〰️

DEVELOPMENT

DEVELOPMENT—SECTION I 〰️

34

36

2nd RETURN PRINCIPAL THEME—PART I ᚙᚙᚙᚙᚙᚙ

BRIDGE PASSAGE ᚙᚙᚙᚙᚙ

CODA

CODA—SECTION I ᚙᚙᚙᚙᚙ

BRIDGE PASSAGE ~~~~~ PRINCIPAL THEME—

PART III, 1st PERIOD ~~~~~~~~~~~~~~~

TRIO

SUBORDINATE THEME—PART I, 1st PERIOD ~~~~~~ SUB-

PRINCIPAL THEME—PART III, 2nd PERIOD

ORDINATE THEME—PART I, 2nd PERIOD ~~~~~~~~~~~ SUB-

ORDINATE THEME—PART II ~~~~~~~~~~~~~~~~

IV

SUBORDINATE THEME—PART I 〰〰〰〰〰〰〰〰〰〰

50

52

SUBORDINATE THEME—PART II 〰〰〰〰〰〰〰〰

CONCLUDING THEME (CODETTA)

DE-

VELOPMENT

VELOPMENT—SECTION 1

DEVELOPMENT—SECTION 2

DEVELOPMENT—SECTION 3